MONTHLY
PLANNER

MO

TO DO LIST

IDEAS

NOTES

TUE		
MON		
SUN		
SAT		
FRI		
THU		
WED		

MONTHLY PLANNER

MONTH:

TO DO LIST

IDEAS

NOTES

TUE

MON

SUN

SAT

FRI

THU

WED

MONTHLY PLANNER

MONTH:

TO DO LIST

_____

_____

_____

_____

IDEAS

NOTES

_____

_____

_____

TUE		
MON		
SUN		
SAT		
FRI		
THU		
WED		

MONTHLY PLANNER

MONTH:

TO DO LIST

IDEAS

NOTES

TUE

MON

SUN

SAT

FRI

THU

WED

MONTHLY PLANNER

MONTH:

TO DO LIST

....
....
....
....

IDEAS

NOTES

....
....
....

TUE		
MON		
SUN		
SAT		
FRI		
THU		
WED		

MONTHLY PLANNER

MONTH:

TO DO LIST

IDEAS

NOTES

TUE		
MON		
SUN		
SAT		
FRI		
THU		
WED		

MONTHLY PLANNER

TO DO LIST

IDEAS

NOTES

MONTH:

TUE		
MON		
SUN		
SAT		
FRI		
THU		
WED		

MONTHLY PLANNER

MONTH:

_____

_____

_____

_____

IDEAS

_____

_____

_____

NOTES

_____

_____

TUE		
MON		
SUN		
SAT		
FRI		
THU		
WED		

MONTHLY
PLANNER

TO DO LIST

_____

_____

_____

_____

IDEAS

NOTES

_____

_____

MONTH:

TUE		
MON		
SUN		
SAT		
FRI		
THU		
WED		

MONTHLY PLANNER

MONTH:

TO DO LIST

....

....

....

....

IDEAS

NOTES

....

....

....

TUE		
MON		
SUN		
SAT		
FRI		
THU		
WED		

YEAR: 2022-2023

MONTHLY PLANNER

MONTH:

TO DO LIST

_____

_____

_____

_____

IDEAS

NOTES

_____

TUE	
MON	
SUN	
SAT	
FRI	
THU	
WED	

MONTHLY PLANNER

TO DO LIST

IDEAS

NOTES

MONTH:

TUE		
MON		
SUN		
SAT		
FRI		
THU		
WED		

YEAR: 2022-2023

Made in the USA
Coppell, TX
23 December 2022

90628166R00015